E IS FOR EASTER

To the children in my life;
may you always know the real reason
to celebrate Easter.
M.

Cover: *In His Hands* © Kathryn Fincher. For more information, go to www.kathyfincher.com.
  Dear to the Heart of the Shepherd © Simon Dewey. Courtesy of Altus Fine Art. For print information, go to www.altusfineart.com.
Page iv–1: *Easter Day* © David McClellan. Referencing *Kids on Easter Egg Hunt* © FamVeld. Courtesy of istock.com.
Page 2: *Come Follow Me* © Sandra Rast. For more information, go to www.sandrarast.com.
Page 3: *Flowers for Mother* by Donald Zolan © 2018 Pemberton & Oakes, Ltd. For print information, go to www.poart.com.
Pages 4–5: *Painting Eggs* © David McClellan. Referencing *Two Little Boys Wearing Easter Bunny Ears* © romrodinka. Courtesy of istock.com
Page 6: *Gethsemane* © James C. Christensen. For print information, go to www.jameschristensenart.com.
Page 7: *Golgotha* © Derek Hegsted. For more information, go to www.hegsted.com.
Pages 8–9: *Dear to the Heart of the Shepherd* © Simon Dewey. Courtesy of Altus Fine Art. For print information, go to www.altusfineart.com.
Page 10–11: *Spring Fever* © Terry Redlin, courtesy of Wild Wings, LLC. www.wildwings.com.
Pages 12: *Feed My Sheep* © J. Bryant Ward. For more information, go to www.JBWstudios.com.
Pages 13: *My Redeemer Lives* © Roger Loveless. For more information, go to www.rogerlovelessart.com.
Pages 14–15: *The First Morning* © Robert Duncan. For more information, go to www.robertduncanstudios.com.
Page 16: *O My Father* © Simon Dewey. Courtesy of Altus Fine Art. For print information, go to www.altusfineart.com.
Page 17: *Triumphal Entry* © Liz Lemon Swindle. Used with permission from Lighthaven. For print information, go to www.lighthaven.net or call 800.366.2781.
Pages 18: *Garden Harvest* © Jean Monti. For more information, go to www.jeanmonti.com.
Page 19: *Son of the Highest* © Joseph F. Brickey. For more information, go to www.josephbrickey.com.
Page 20–21: *Garden Tomb* by Jon McNaughton © McNaughton Fine Art Co. For more information, go to jonmcnaughton.com.
Pages 22–23: *Three Maids a Wading* © J. Bryant Ward. For more information, go to www.JBWstudios.com.
Page 24: *The Hands of Christ* © Spencer Williams. For more information, go to www.jesuspaintings.com.
Page 25: *Country Friends* by Donald Zolan © 2018 Pemberton & Oakes, Ltd. For more information, go towww.poart.com.
Pages 26: *Life's a Dance* © Robert Duncan. For more information, go to www.robertduncanstudios.com.
Pages 27: *In His Hands* © Kathryn Fincher. For more information, go to www.kathyfincher.com.
Page 28: *Out for a Ride* © Robert Duncan. For more information, go to www.robertduncanstudios.com.

Cover design copyright © 2018 by Covenant Communications, Inc.
Jacket and book designed by Christina Marcano © 2018 Covenant Communications

Published by Covenant Communications, Inc.
American Fork, Utah

Printed in the United States of America
First Printing: March 2018

24 23 22 21 20 19 18   10 9 8 7 6 5 4 3 2 1

ISBN-13: 978-1-52440-570-0

E IS FOR EASTER

M. Weber Longoria

A is for April,
a month of rebirth,
when new life Abounds
and Awakens the earth.

B is for Bouquets,
Baskets, and a Bunny
and honey Bees Buzzing
now the days have turned sunny.

 is for Candy and Chocolate galore
but mostly for Christ, who opened death's door.

 is for Daffodil, tulip, and lily
that Delight us by blooming while the earth is still chilly.

E is for Easter Eggs
dyed Every color
and hidden all over
for us to discover.

F is for Family,
neighbors, and Friends
who join us for Fun
as wintertime ends.

 is for the Garden of Gethsemane,

where the Savior atoned for you and for me.

H is for the Hill where Christ Hung on the cross;

for our entrance to Heaven, He alone paid the cost.

I is an Invitation to come follow the Lord
and Invest your life in His eternal reward.

J is for Jesus,
our Brother and Savior,
and for Jelly beans
of each color and flavor.

K is for Kindness
as friendship begins
and for Kites that fly high
in blustering winds.

Terry Redlin © 1992

L is for Lambs who are lost and alone,
   then found by the Lord, who will shepherd them home.

M is for the Miracle of the risen Master
   witnessed by Mary the third Morning after.

N is for Newborn babes
found lying at rest
and for Noisy spring chicks
cuddled up in a Nest.

O is for the Olive grove where Christ went to pray
to atone for Our sins, to take them away.

P is for the narrow Path made of Palm leaves
for the Prince of Peace by those who believe.

 is for Quick as the Quest is begun;
find what is hidden, and share in the fun.

 is for the Risen Lord, who on Easter day
was first Resurrected to show us the way.

S is for the Savior,
who Sacrificed His life
and gave us our Salvation
to conquer worldly Strife.

T is for Triumph
over death and Tomb.
Heaven greets the sinner
because of Christ's wounds.

U is for Umbrellas Under spring rains
refreshing earth's bounties, from flowers to grains.

V is for the Vivid Voices of songbirds that sing
and for Christ's Victory as Master and King.

W is for Warmth as the World Wakes to spring
and the Wonder and joy that new life can bring.

X is for eXcitement for eXcellent weather,
  to eXplore the outdoors and spend time together.

Y is for Yellow, like the light from the sun;
  as we Yearn for Christ's love, it warms everyone.

Z is for Zigging and Zagging and Zipping,
for hippity hopping and biking and skipping.